COCOA WARRIORS

Written by
ALEKSANDAR PANEV

Illustrated by
KARINE CHARLEBOIS

This story is set in the 16th century, in the country we now call Mexico. Each chapter ends with a non-fiction page that gives more information about real people's lives and actual events at that time.

OXFORD
UNIVERSITY PRESS

HERNÁN CORTÉS

DOÑA MARINA

MONTEZUMA II

VAKAKI

REAL PEOPLE IN HISTORY

HERNÁN CORTÉS (1485–1547): The Spanish conquistador who was sent to conquer Mexico for Spain.

DOÑA MARINA (1505–1551): A young indigenous woman who became Cortés' interpreter.

MONTEZUMA II (1480–1520): An Aztec king who had to defend his empire against the Spanish.

FICTIONAL CHARACTER

VAKAKI: A young Tabascan boy who wants to fight for his tribe's freedom from the Aztecs.

Contents

In 1492, with the voyage of Christopher Columbus, the Spanish learned about the existence of a 'new land' across the ocean. They began to send more explorers there, and hoped to conquer it for themselves. However, the New World wasn't empty and available – it was already inhabited by many different groups of indigenous peoples.

Hernán Cortés

In 1519, a Spanish adventurer named Hernán Cortés led a small army into what is now Mexico. It was the home of a large and powerful civilisation called the Aztecs.

1492	1502	1514	10 Feb. 1519	8 Nov. 1519
Christopher Columbus reaches America.	Montezuma II becomes the emperor of the Aztec Empire.	The Spanish conquer Cuba and establish a base there.	Hernán Cortés leaves for Mexico from Cuba.	Cortés and his army enter the Aztec capital city, Tenochtitlán. Cortés takes Montezuma prisoner shortly after.

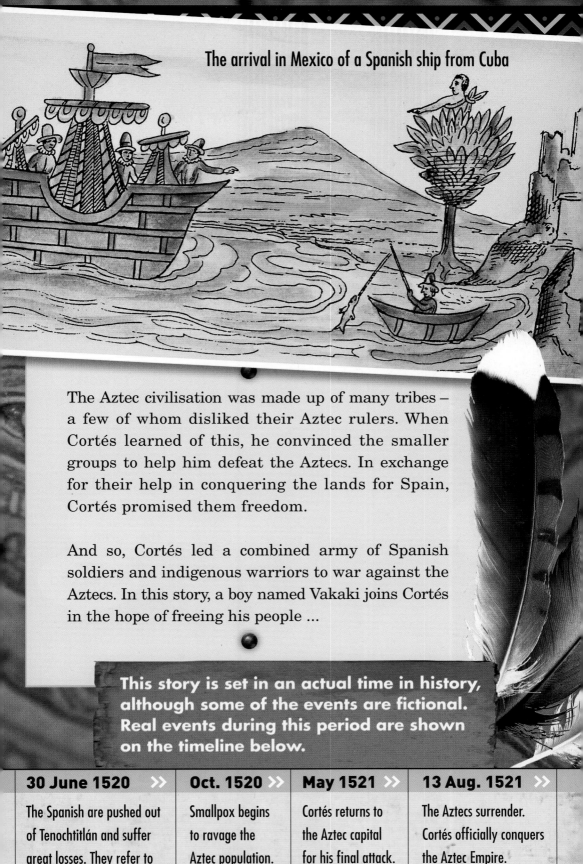

The arrival in Mexico of a Spanish ship from Cuba

The Aztec civilisation was made up of many tribes – a few of whom disliked their Aztec rulers. When Cortés learned of this, he convinced the smaller groups to help him defeat the Aztecs. In exchange for their help in conquering the lands for Spain, Cortés promised them freedom.

And so, Cortés led a combined army of Spanish soldiers and indigenous warriors to war against the Aztecs. In this story, a boy named Vakaki joins Cortés in the hope of freeing his people ...

This story is set in an actual time in history, although some of the events are fictional. Real events during this period are shown on the timeline below.

30 June 1520 »	Oct. 1520 »	May 1521 »	13 Aug. 1521 »
The Spanish are pushed out of Tenochtitlán and suffer great losses. They refer to this event as *La Noche Triste* (the Night of Sorrows).	Smallpox begins to ravage the Aztec population.	Cortés returns to the Aztec capital for his final attack.	The Aztecs surrender. Cortés officially conquers the Aztec Empire.

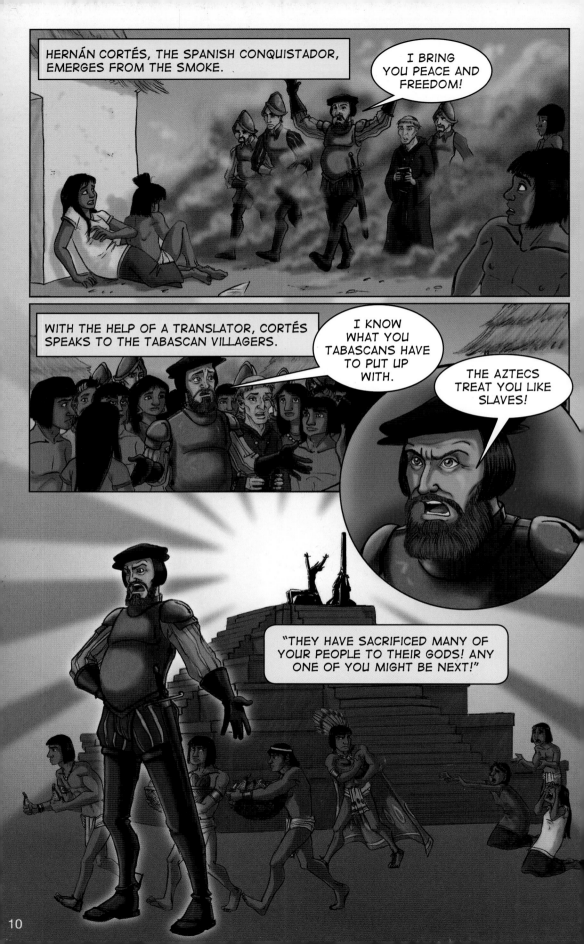

QUETZALCOATL

TIME OUT!

Quetzalcoatl (ket-sahl-koh-aht-ul) was also known as the Feathered Serpent. He was a central figure in Aztec and Mayan mythology. He was the Lord of Life and represented the forces of good and light.

He was both the morning and evening star, and the symbol of both death and resurrection. According to one myth, Quetzalcoatl gathered the bones of all the ancient dead. When he dripped his own blood on these bones, the humans of this present universe were born.

Snake-shaped sceptre — a symbol of purification

Headdress made of jaguar fur, decorated with precious stones and quetzal feathers

Red and bird-like mask — to identify him as the god of wind

Twisted shell ear caps — a symbol of fertility

Wind jewel made from a conch, worn from his neck — a symbol of life's divine breath

Belt with discs representing the precious blood drawn from humans

WHAT'S GOING ON OVER THERE?

TO PLEASE HIS NEW SPANISH ALLIES, THE TABASCAN CHIEF OFFERS SLAVES TO CORTÉS.

THE WOMEN GIVEN TO CORTÉS ARE BAPTIZED. THEY BECOME CATHOLICS.

AND YOU SHALL NOW BE KNOWN AS DOÑA MARINA.

16

VAKAKI AND MARINA QUICKLY
BECOME GOOD FRIENDS.

SEVERAL WEEKS LATER, AS CORTÉS AND HIS NEW ALLIES ARE MARCHING TOWARDS THE AZTEC CITY, THEY'RE STOPPED BY ANOTHER TRIBE IN THE AREA.

MARINA! TELL ME, WHO ARE THESE MEN?

THEY'RE ENVOYS FROM THE CHOLULA TRIBE NEARBY.

THEY'RE INVITING YOU TO THEIR VILLAGE.

GREAT! TELL THEM TO GO AHEAD AND WE'LL FOLLOW.

MARINA HAS LEARNED SPANISH QUICKLY. SHE IS THE INTERPRETER FOR CORTÉS.

MARINA OVERHEARS THE ENVOYS WHISPERING IN THEIR OWN LANGUAGE.

OH, NO! WE CAN'T GO WITH THEM.

WHY NOT?

THEY'RE PREPARING TO AMBUSH US!

AFTER MONTHS OF MARCHING, CORTÉS AND HIS ARMY ARRIVE AT THE EDGE OF THE AZTEC CITY.
HOW BEAUTIFUL! THERE'S NO OTHER CITY LIKE THIS IN THE WHOLE WORLD.
THIS MUST BE A DREAM!
THE AZTECS WILL SURELY SEE US COMING!
WILL WE BE ABLE TO DEFEAT THEM?
DON'T WORRY, EVERYTHING IS IN OUR FAVOUR.

CONQUISTADORS

C onquistador (con-KEES-ta-dor) means 'conqueror' in Spanish. Conquistadors conquered much of the Americas and Asia-Pacific on behalf of Spain between the 15th and 17th centuries. Many conquistadors were poor which is why they left Spain to seek their fortunes.

Juan Ponce de León

There are many famous conquistadors in history:

- Christopher Columbus was the first Spanish conquistador. He sailed to modern-day Cuba and established a settlement there in 1492.

- Juan Ponce de León was the first European known to have visited what is now North America in 1513.

- Francisco Pizarro conquered the Inca Empire and founded the city of Lima, now capital of Peru, in 1535.

Many people considered the conquistadors very successful at the time of their conquests. Others did not agree. The conquistadors discovered new lands for Spain, but many of them also brought disease and death to the indigenous peoples of these lands. What do you think about what they did?

8 NOVEMBER 1519: THE SPANISH PREPARE TO ENTER THE CITY OF THE AZTECS.

ARE THEY GOING TO ATTACK US?

I DOUBT IT. IF THEY WERE GOING TO ATTACK THEY WOULD HAVE ALREADY.

LOOK — THE EMPEROR OF THE AZTECS!

WELL, WELL, WELL. MONTEZUMA, WE MEET AT LAST.

THE EMPEROR USUALLY NEVER LEAVES HIS PALACE. THIS IS A GREAT HONOUR FOR US!

THE SPANISH MAKE MONTEZUMA A PRISONER IN HIS OWN CITY.

NEWS OF MONTEZUMA'S CAPTURE TRAVELS FAST.

MARINA! I JUST HEARD ABOUT MONTEZUMA!

28

TIME OUT!

Aztec warriors were brave fighters who were well trained and organised for battle. They considered warfare a religious duty. Their goal was not only to defeat their opponents, but to capture as many of them alive as possible. After a battle, the warriors sacrificed prisoners to the Aztec gods.

Aztec warriors used weapons such as bows and arrows, spears, clubs and swords. These weapons were mostly made from wood. Some had pieces of stone embedded in the wood.

Mexican warriors fight the Spanish, 1520

The Aztec army had a force of special warriors called the Jaguar and the Eagle Knights. These warriors had proved their skill and worth on the battlefield. The Jaguar and Eagle Knights wore special uniforms and helmets and were the most feared of all Aztec warriors.

THE SPANISH AND THE AZTECS FIGHT BRAVELY.

THOUSANDS ARE DEFEATED ON BOTH SIDES.

THOUSANDS OF AZTEC WARRIORS ARE WAITING TO AMBUSH THE SPANISH!

BUT THE AZTECS HAVE MADE A MISTAKE.

CHARGE!

THEIR POSITION ON LOWER GROUND LEAVES THEM OPEN TO ATTACK.

CORTÉS BREAKS THROUGH THE AZTEC LINE. IT'S A SPANISH VICTORY!

FROM COCOA TO CHOCOLATE

1500–400 BC/BCE
The Olmecs are believed to have been the first to grow cocoa beans as a crop.

AD/CE 250–900
The Mayans perfect an unsweetened and bitter cocoa drink. They establish the earliest known cocoa plantations in Mexico.

1000–1400s
The ruling Aztecs demand taxes in the form of cocoa beans. They begin to make their own cocoa drink.

1502
Christopher Columbus comes across a Mayan trading canoe carrying cocoa beans. He sends some back to Italy.

1519
Hernán Cortés is introduced to the Aztec cocoa drink. He establishes a cocoa plantation for Spain and takes some cocoa beans back to Spain with him in 1528.

1585
First official shipment of cocoa beans arrives in Spain from Mexico. The Spanish begin to make their own cocoa drinks, adding cane sugar and vanilla.

1657
The first shop selling the new 'chocolate drink' to the masses opens in London.

1847
An English company introduces the chocolate we know best today — solid chocolate bars!

NINE MONTHS AFTER THE BATTLE AT OTUMBA ...

IT'S THE AZTECS' TURN TO TREMBLE BEFORE OUR FORCES.

CORTÉS IS BACK TO CAPTURE THE AZTEC CITY WITH A BIGGER, BETTER ARMY.

WE'RE SURE TO TAKE THE CITY THIS TIME.

I HEAR THAT MANY AZTECS HAVE DIED FROM A MYSTERIOUS ILLNESS.

IT'S SMALLPOX.

YES, SMALLPOX ... MY UNEXPECTED ALLY!

BWA-HA-HA-HA!

THE SPANISH ATTACK ON THE CITY LASTS ALMOST THREE MONTHS.

THEY CUT OFF THE AZTECS' FOOD AND WATER SUPPLIES.

THEY BURN AND DESTROY EVERYTHING IN THEIR WAY.

THE AZTECS HAVE NO CHOICE BUT TO SURRENDER.

THE AFTERMATH

O nce the Spanish had conquered the Aztec empire, it was the beginning of the end for the indigenous population of Central and South America.

When Cortés and his Spanish army arrived in 1519, the indigenous population numbered about 22 million. By the end of the century, only two million remained.

In 1565, a Spanish royal judge wrote about the effect Cortés had on the land and the people he conquered:

1565

"It is certain that ... in the seven years, more or less, that he conquered and governed it, the natives suffered many deaths, and many terrible dealings, robberies and oppressions were inflicted on them, taking advantage of their persons and their lands, without order, weight nor measure ... The people diminished in great number, as much due to excessive taxes and mistreatment, as to illness and smallpox, such that now a very great and notable fraction of the people are gone."

MESO MIX

Mayan pyramid at Chichén-Itzá

Central and South America changed a great deal with the arrival of the Spanish and, later, the Portuguese.

Many indigenous nations and peoples, such as the Aztecs, Mayans and Incas, disappeared. The Europeans destroyed entire cities and civilisations. In some cases, these civilisations had been more advanced than the Europeans.

Many of the European settlers married local indigenous women. They also tried to convert the indigenous population to Catholicism. Doña Marina, who features in this story, was just one of many who were baptized and given new Christian names.

Over time, new societies emerged here. They were very different from the indigenous nations.

However, some of the old ways are still alive today in the form of local festivals and beliefs. Even though Spanish and Portuguese became the dominant languages in these societies, there is a new interest in learning native languages.

In 1821, after three centuries of foreign rule, Mexico regained its independence from Spain. Every year, Mexicans celebrate their independence day, called *El Grito de Independencia* (Cry of Independence), on 16 September.

Head of a serpent column
on a temple in Chichén-Itzá

INDEX

GLOSSARY

ambush – a surprise attack by people who have hidden themselves

civilisation – a society or culture that is highly developed

conquer – to defeat

explorer – a person who travels through a country to learn about it

freedom – being free

indigenous – to come from, be a native of, a particular place

interpreter – a person who translates what someone says into another language

native – a person born in a particular place

sacrifice – to give up or offer a thing or person so that something good might happen

surrender – to stop fighting and admit defeat

tribe – a group of families living in one area and ruled by a chief

warrior – a person who fights in a battle

weapon – something used to harm or kill people in a battle